If I Could Drive a Tonka Truck!

If I Could Drive a Fire Truck!

If I Could Drive a Dump Truck!

If I Could Drive a Loader!

If I Could Drive a Bulldozer!

If I Could Drive an Ambulance!

If I Could Drive a Tow Truck!

If I Could Drive a Crane!

If I Could Drive a Grader!

SCHOLASTIC INC.

New York   Toronto   London   Auckland   Sydney
Mexico City   New Delhi   Hong Kong   Buenos Aires

IF I COULD DRIVE A
FIRE TRUCK!

by Michael Teitelbaum
Illustrated by Uldis Klavins and Jeff Walker

My name is Susan.
Today, I'm going to visit Grandma with my mom and dad.
It's a long drive, but I've got my favorite fire truck to play with.

WHEE-OOH! WHEE-OOH! WHEE-OOH!
A real fire truck races past us on its way to an emergency.
My dad moves our car out of the way and slows down.
Wow, look at that fire truck go!
What if *I* could drive a fire truck?

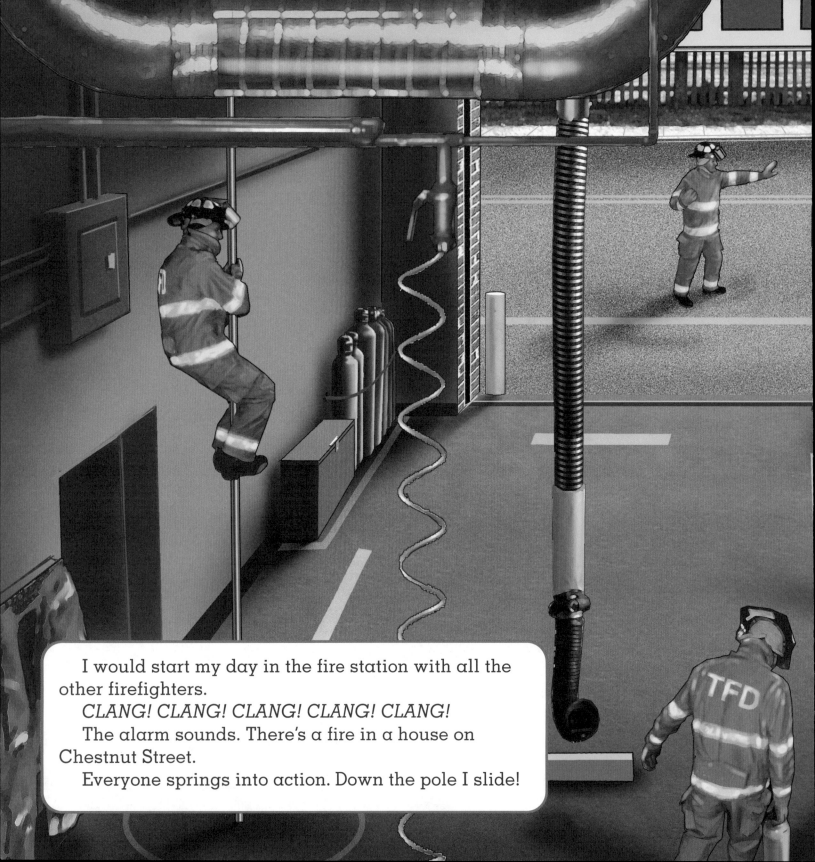

I would start my day in the fire station with all the other firefighters.

CLANG! CLANG! CLANG! CLANG! CLANG!

The alarm sounds. There's a fire in a house on Chestnut Street.

Everyone springs into action. Down the pole I slide!

We race to our ladder truck. The ladder can go up to reach high windows. Our truck also carries hoses for water and axes and saws for getting into burning buildings.

Some of the firefighters stand on the truck's back bumper. They hold onto handles so they don't fall off. I drive.

I speed through the streets with my siren screaming. *WHEE-OOH! WHEE-OOH! WHEE-OOH!*
The other cars get out of my way. They know I'm racing to fight a fire, and every second counts!

In a few minutes, we arrive at the fire. The top floor of a house is burning. Flames and smoke pour from the windows. The family who lives there has gotten out safely. Now it's up to us to save their home.

A police car screeches to a halt. The fire chief's truck is right behind it. Police officers keep the crowd safely away from the fire. The fire chief directs the firefighters as we battle the blaze.

I attach one end of my hose to the fire hydrant. Once the hydrant is opened, water will rush through the hose.

Next, we raise our tall ladder all the way up to the windows on the top floor of the house.

I climb up the ladder. When I reach the nozzle at the top, I aim it at the flames.
WHOOSH!
A powerful stream of water pours from the nozzle.

Soon the flames are gone. The fire is out, and the building is saved.

The family thanks us for saving their home. Then the fire chief sends us back to the fire station.
Good job, firefighters!

Here we are, at Grandma's house at last!
I can't wait to tell her about all the brave things I
would do, if I could drive a fire truck.

IF I COULD DRIVE A
DUMP TRUCK!

by Michael Teitelbaum
Illustrated by Uldis Klavins

First I fill the truck with sand. Then I lift the truck's bed and dump the sand out.

What if *I* could drive a dump truck?

The great thing about my dump truck is that I can unload it without help from anyone else!

I press a lever in the cab. Then the bed lifts up and the gravel pours out.

My dump truck and I help at the site of a new building. Sometimes big loads of dirt need to be moved from one part of a construction site to another.

Another truck, called a loader, fills my dump truck with dirt.

Next, my dump truck and I help landscapers make a beautiful garden. First my dump truck carries in a load of topsoil.

Then I dump a load of wood mulch. The mulch is made from shredded branches that have been trimmed from trees. It protects the topsoil.

Finally, my dump truck dumps a load of large stepping stones. The landscapers will use these stones to create a path through the garden.

IF I COULD DRIVE A
LOADER!

by Michael Teitelbaum
Illustrated by Uldis Klavins

My name is Ricky, and I love trucks.
I really like playing with my toy trucks and reading books about trucks. That's how I learn all about the ways trucks work.
My favorite truck is the loader.

Today is a special day. I look out the window and see a loader show up, right in front of my house! It's here to dig a ditch for new pipes in the neighborhood.

Wow! Look at that loader pick up big piles of dirt.

What if *I* could drive a loader?

Then I would pour the dirt into a dump truck.

My loader has big wheels. They roll right over rocks and bumpy ground.

Today my neighbors want to plant a new tree in their yard. The tree is much too heavy to move without a big truck. No problem! My loader carries the tree to its new home.

Our town just put in a new baseball field. Now we need a new road to make it easy for people to get there. My loader helps build the road.

First, a truck called a grader makes a smooth path for the new road. Then it's my turn! My loader scoops up the loose dirt and carries it to a dump truck.

Now for the gravel!

At a quarry, my loader shovels gravel into the dump truck. Now the gravel can be spread on the new road. Then the road can be paved.

Next, I use my loader to help a farmer. He needs to prepare a new field to plant his crops.

First, I scrape the grass off the field. I like watching the grass roll into the bucket!

My loader levels the farmer's field. I dig up the high spots and add dirt to the low spots. Finally, the whole field is even. Now the farmer can plow and plant!

In the winter, my loader helps out during a big snowstorm. The plow truck is ready to clear snow from the roads. But it needs salt and sand to spread on the road after it plows. The salt and sand will make the snowy roads less slippery.

There's a big pile of salt and a big pile of sand inside the garage. I fill half of my bucket with salt. Then I'll move to the next pile and scoop up some sand.

With me at the controls, my loader brings the salt and sand out to the plow truck. I dump the mixture into the truck. Then I go back for more.

When the plow truck is full, the driver heads out to plow. After he plows, he'll spread salt and sand on the road.

Uh-oh! The dump truck driver is stuck behind a big pile of snow. He can't get his dump truck out.

But my loader can scoop up and move large mounds of snow! In no time, I dig through the mountain of snow. The dump truck is free!

I would help lots of people, if I could drive a loader.
Maybe someday, I'll get to drive a real one!

IF I COULD DRIVE A
BULLDOZER!

by Michael Teitelbaum
Illustrated by Uldis Klavins

My name is Matt, and I really love playing with trucks.

My favorite truck is the bulldozer.

I play with my toy bulldozer in the backyard, pushing dirt and rocks around.

What if *I* could drive a bulldozer?

A bulldozer can weigh as much as ten tons! It is like a tank with a large steel blade on the front. A bulldozer doesn't have wheels. It rolls on special crawler treads.

The treads make it easy for the bulldozer to roll over rough ground. They also help hold up the bulldozer's heavy weight. That way, the weight is spread over a big area, so the bulldozer doesn't sink into the mud.

My bulldozer's sharp blade stays close to the ground, cutting through even the hardest soil.

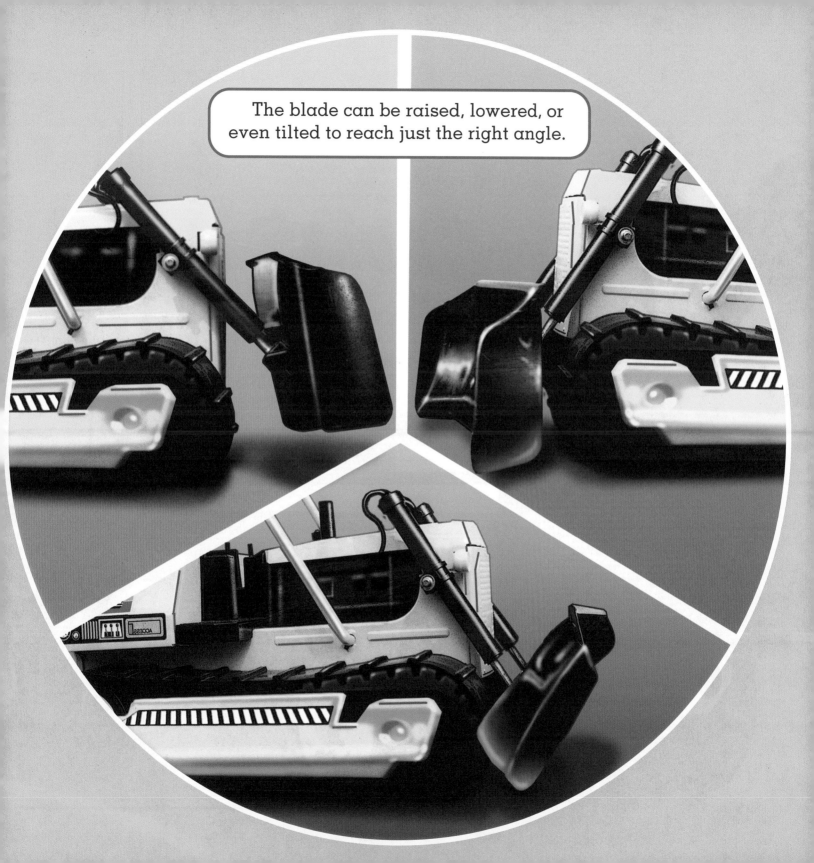

Because of its crawler treads, a bulldozer can't ride on the road like other trucks. I drive my bulldozer onto the back of a big truck called a tractor trailer. Then the tractor trailer drives along paved roads, carrying the bulldozer. That's how I get my bulldozer to the job site.

Today I am helping a farmer by knocking down his old barn. Then I'll help prepare the site for a new barn to be built.

The old barn was starting to fall down on its own, and it was too dangerous to use anymore. Working carefully, my bulldozer helps to push down the rest of the crumbling building.

Then I push the broken pieces of the barn away to make room for the new one.

Finally, I use the bottom of the bulldozer's blade to push the dirt and smooth out the ground.
Now the new barn can be built!

The bulldozer's work is done now.
Some other trucks arrive. Here comes a loader to scoop, a backhoe to dig, and a dump truck to carry away the wood from the old barn.

IF I COULD DRIVE AN
AMBULANCE!

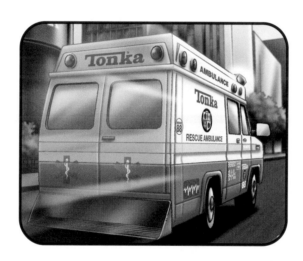

by Michael Teitelbaum
Cover Illustrated by Tom LaPadula
Interiors illustrated by Isidre Mones and Marc Mones

For EMT workers past, present, and future—heroes all.
Special thanks to Peter Auricchio for giving freely of his time and expertise.

I imagine that I'm racing through the streets. My emergency lights are flashing and my siren is blaring.

What if I could drive an ambulance?

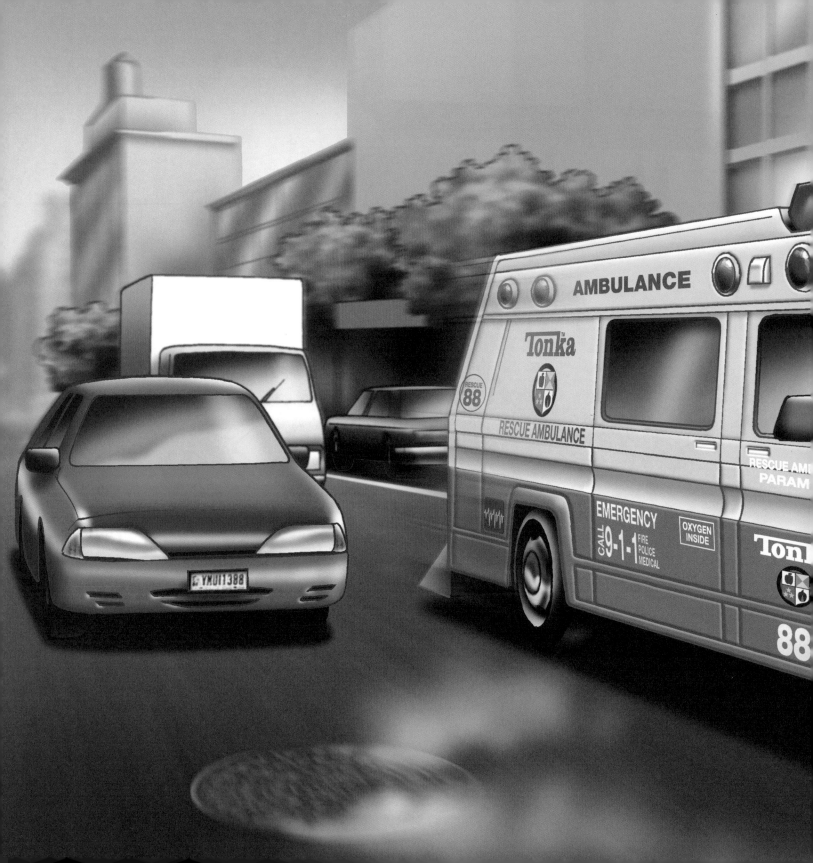

Every ambulance has two people. My partner is named Dina. We are both trained emergency medical technicians. We're called EMTs for short.

Someone has called 911 to report an emergency. A dispatcher — the person who got that call — contacts the ambulance driver closest to the emergency.

That's me!

Cars pull over and let me pass.

I have to be careful to slow down at red lights and stop signs.

The ambulance dashboard has switches to control the lights and siren.

I also have a computer that provides me with information. It tells me about the injured woman, and it gives directions so that I can reach her quickly.

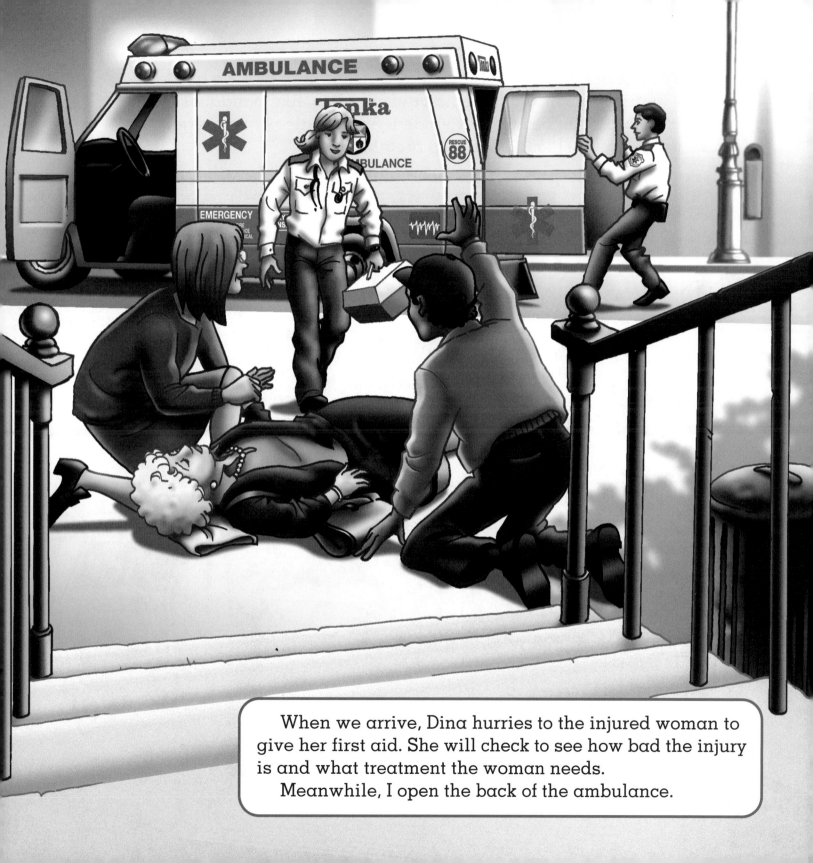

When we arrive, Dina hurries to the injured woman to give her first aid. She will check to see how bad the injury is and what treatment the woman needs.

Meanwhile, I open the back of the ambulance.

We have lots of equipment. There is a stretcher here that we use to carry the injured person. We have first aid supplies, like bandages, so that we can help if the person is wounded. And we also have oxygen in case the injured person needs help breathing.

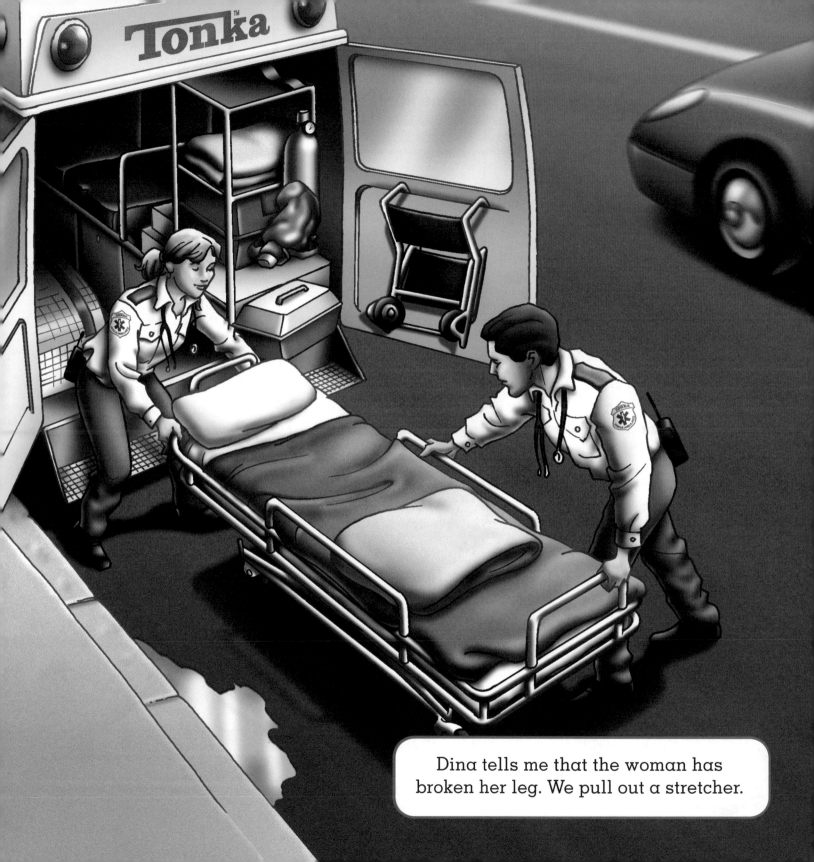

Dina tells me that the woman has broken her leg. We pull out a stretcher.

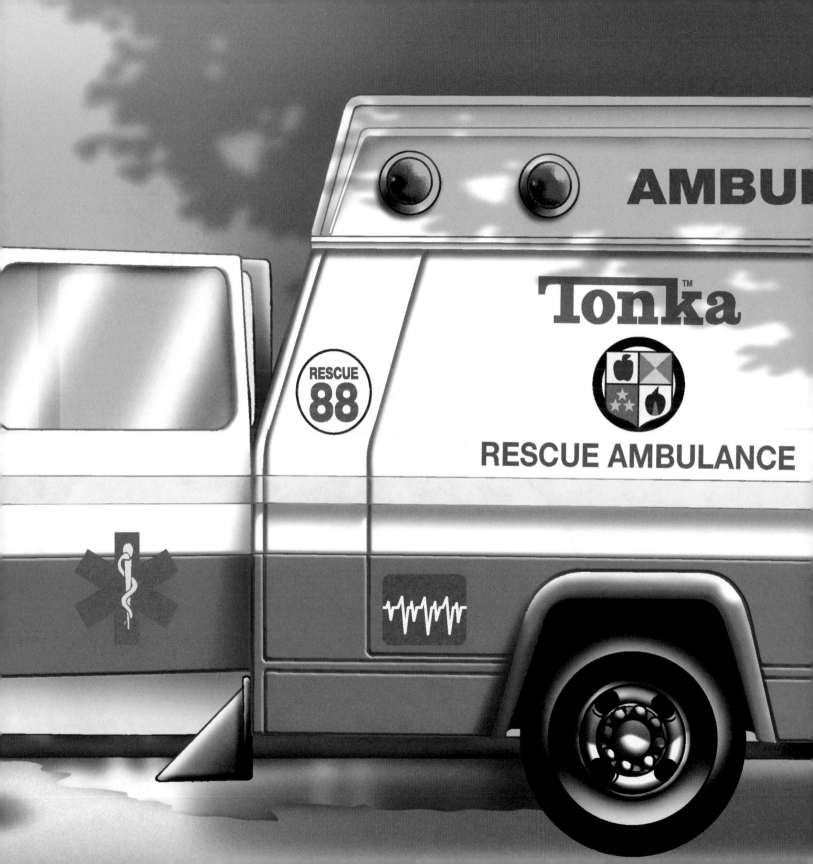

Dina rides in the back to make sure the injured woman is all right.
I drive quickly to the nearest hospital.

At the hospital, doctors and nurses take over.
They'll take good care of the injured woman.

I would help lots of people if I could drive an ambulance!

IF I COULD DRIVE A
TOW TRUCK!

by Michael Teitelbaum
Illustrated by Jesus Redondo & digitally painted by Steve Mitchell

What if I could drive a tow truck?

My tow truck has a powerful engine in the front. I need lots of power to pull heavy cars, trucks, and buses.

When a car breaks down on the road, my tow truck and I swing into action!

I back my tow truck into position. Then I unwind the cable from the winch. Next, I attach the hook to the front of the broken-down car.

As the motor continues to turn the spool, the cable lifts up the front of the car. Now it's ready to be towed.

I get back into the tow truck and tow the car to a repair shop. The driver rides with me in my truck. Soon his car will be back on the road.

My tow truck also helps after accidents. These jobs are called *recoveries*.

This van has flipped over. Luckily, the driver is not hurt. To begin the recovery, I attach the cable to the van.

Using my winch, I carefully roll the van back onto its wheels. Mission accomplished!

In another operation, I help recover a small plane that had to make an emergency landing. The plane ended up in a lake, but I'll have it back on dry land in no time!

Once the cable is attached, I drive forward very slowly. Then, using all of its power, my tow truck pulls the plane from the lake. Hooray!

IF I COULD DRIVE A
CRANE!

by Michael Teitelbaum
Illustrated by Uldis Klavins

I would move heavy loads from one place to another. That's what cranes are for.

There are lots of different kinds of cranes, and I would drive them all!

A truck crane has wheels and can go anywhere a regular truck can go. I drive it on the highway to get to a construction site.

Before I can use my truck crane, I have to put down special legs called outriggers. These strong metal legs help keep the crane steady when I'm lifting big loads.

Now my truck crane is ready to work. I can extend the crane's arm to make it bigger. I can also rotate the crane to move a load from one place to another.

When I attach a big bucket to the end of the crane's main cable, I can use the crane to dig and to move gravel.

A truck has brought huge bundles of lumber to the construction site. I attach grappling tines to the end of the crane's cable. Now my truck crane can unload the lumber. Then I can move it to exactly where it's needed.

By attaching a large magnet to the end of the cable, my truck crane can lift heavy pieces of steel.

Construction beams and girders are the first parts used when a new building is started. With its magnet, the crane can move the parts with no problem.

Another kind of crane is the crawler crane. It doesn't have wheels like a truck crane.

Instead, a crawler crane moves on special treads, just like a bulldozer. These treads help the crawler crane work in soft, muddy areas.

I'm using my crawler crane to help remove fallen trees from this flooded area.

For the biggest and heaviest loads of all, I use a bridge crane. It's also called a gantry crane.

A bridge crane's legs are very tall and far apart.

I use my bridge crane at a seaport. There I unload big, heavy crates from arriving ships. I lift the crates out of the ships, then place them onto flatbed trucks that drive them away.

My bridge crane can swivel to move its load.

It can also move its load by rolling along on tracks, just like a train. But a bridge crane moves slowly, and trains move really fast!

My wrecking crane is used for a very special job. I use it to knock down old walls or crumbling buildings.

A big, heavy wrecking ball hangs from the crane's main cable. Another cable, which I control, pulls the wrecking ball back. When I let the ball go, it swings into the wall and knocks it down.

I'd use all kinds of cranes, for all kinds of jobs, if I could drive a crane!

IF I COULD DRIVE A
GRADER!

by Michael Teitelbaum
Illustrated by Isidre Mones and Mark Mones

My name is Steven. I love to play with my trucks in the sandbox! My favorite truck is a grader.

I pretend that I'm helping to build a new road with my grader. I smooth out the sand so the road is level.

What if I could drive a grader?

My grader has a cab and big wheels. The cab is where I sit so I can operate the grader. The big wheels help me drive over bumpy surfaces.

The grader's blade sits between the front and back wheels. It can be raised or lowered and turned to the left or right.

When a new road needs to be made, a truck called a bulldozer shows up first. The bulldozer moves lots of dirt and big rocks. Then it outlines where the new road will go.

Once the road is outlined, it's time for my grader to go to work.

Using its blade, my grader shapes and smooths the road surface.

I raise and lower the blade depending on how high the dirt is. I want to make the road surface smooth and even.

I also want to make sure that the road is not perfectly flat. Instead, it should slope down from the center to the left and the right. That way, rain runs off the road into drainage ditches.

The road is now ready to be paved!

My grader also helps to make the drainage ditches on the sides of the road. These ditches carry the water safely away after a heavy rain. First a truck called a backhoe digs the drainage ditch.

The cut made by the backhoe is very rough. That's where my grader comes in. I use the blade to smooth out the rough cut. Soon the ditch is done.

That's what I would do
if I could drive a grader!